Introduction

The Learning Disabilities Roadshow

The Learning Disabilities Roadshow project provided introductory-level training for professionals and carers working with young people with learning disabilities in the area of sexuality, sex and relationships and sexual health. The project was managed by **fpa** from April 2002–March 2003 and funded by The PPP Foundation. This training took the form of 15 three-day events for up to 16 participants in different localities around England.

The roadshows went to Surrey, Hampshire, Tower Hamlets, Cornwall, Dover, Islington, Manchester, Enfield, Clapham, Sheffield, Taunton, Stratford, Essex, Harrogate and Cambridge and trained over 200 professionals.

The participants came from a wide variety of statutory and voluntary backgrounds including care workers, carers, community nurses, social services staff, speech and language therapists, health promotion specialists, school nurses and support staff.

The publication

As the roadshows progressed around England it became clear that the variety of expertise and insights that staff who work in the field of learning disabilities bring to their work should be recorded. It became increasingly apparent that to compile a resource that captured both the creative approaches adopted by staff as well as their dilemmas would benefit all those who work with this client group.

This publication describes the issues and concerns that over 200 staff brought with them to the 45 days of training around the country. It encapsulates the discussions and debates from the training and illustrates constructive ways of working. It highlights how a range of staff respond to dilemmas as well as offering information on legislation and health that participants found to be practical and useful.

It brings together the issues and information into a short user friendly guide for staff who want to inform their practice in sex and relationships work with service users.

It includes:

- reasons why this work is so important
- useful tips for everyday work
- guidance on the law
- working with parents, families and carers
- information, awareness and skills needed to develop the worker as a resource
- resource and contact lists.

Terminology

This publication uses the terms 'learning disabilities', 'service user' and 'staff'.

It is acknowledged there are regional variations of these terms used, and 'learning disabilities' is often called 'learning difficulties' which can also have a different meaning.

'Service user' is this publication's term for clients, anyone in the care of a service.

'Staff' covers all course participants which includes job roles such as care workers, carers, community nurses, social services staff, speech and language therapists, health promotion specialists, school nurses and support staff.

All the quotes used throughout the publication are from staff who attended the training, unless otherwise referenced.

Contents

Acknowledgements

Thank you to everyone who hosted a roadshow and special thanks to the organisers:

Denise Souter, Surrey Oaklands NHS Trust
Greg Clare, Surrey Hampshire Borders NHS Trust
Jim Fagan, Tower Hamlets PCT
Paul Hancock, Cornwall Partnership NHS Trust
Mary Thomas, East Kent Community NHS Trust
Pat Jackson, Community Practitioners and Health Visitors Association
Tim Plant, Salford PCT
Karen Harms, The Enfield Society
Helen Peters, The Southside Partnership
Rob Brown, Sheffield Centre for HIV and Sexual Health
Rachel Pike, Julian Hallett and Victoria Ralfs, South West Downs Syndrome Association
Helen Larder, Stratford and District Mencap
Christine Mortimer and Lauren Mackay, Barking and Dagenham Social Services
Rachel Davies, Yorkshire and Humberside Downs Syndrome Association
Jim Thomas and Sandy Hunt, Cambridgeshire Learning Disability Partnership.

And thank you to all the trainers:

Sarah Andrews, Angie Brown-Simpson, Johnny Coleman, Sabnum Dharamsi,
Deryl Dix, Greg Falola, Jean Gawlinski, Ian Scott, Juliana Slobodian and Marilyn Tew.

And those who helped with and commented on this publication:

Angie Brown-Simpson, Simon de Carteret, Claire Etienne, Christine Mills,
Juliana Slobodian and Terri Ryland.

And finally thank you to The PPP Foundation for providing the funding for this
project to go ahead.

Why is this work so important?

People with learning disabilities have traditionally faced discrimination. To deny that a person with a learning disability is a sexual being is to treat them less fully as a person. Avoiding this area of work, for whatever reason, can contribute to the discrimination people with learning disabilities face. This is not only an ethical but a professional practice issue.

It is therefore essential that staff find ways of exploring appropriate public and private behaviour such as shows of affection, masturbation or seeking consent in relationships to enable service users to understand their rights and the law.

If service users are unable to recognise what is non-consensual or abusive behaviour and, because of this are unaware of their right to signal (verbally or otherwise) "no", they are at greater risk of being sexually abused.

During the roadshows some staff discussed evidence of historical sexual abuse disclosed by their older service users. This highlighted the importance of education for children and young people. It needs to be recognised that some will abuse others as this is the behaviour they have learnt from personal experience. These issues should be addressed openly and as early as possible with children and young people who have been abused to increase their personal awareness and responsibility and reduce the risk of them progressing from victim to abuser.

"I have learnt that people with learning disabilities are not dissimiliar to those without, but simply have different issues that are often imposed upon them due to circumstance, not as daunting as I at first thought!"

One of the biggest reasons sexuality work is avoided centres on fear. It relates to vulnerable people being sexually exploited or abused and the idea that they need to be 'protected' from their sexuality. The potential for embarrassment, lack of awareness and the inappropriate influence of personal attitudes and beliefs were issues which the roadshow aimed to combat by helping staff develop knowledge, skills, awareness and strategies for effective work. It emphasised that this work is not an optional 'add on', but it is fundamental to the development of any individual with or without a learning disability.

All people share basic rights:

- to be independent
- to be treated with dignity and respect
- to be able to exercise basic human rights
- to be accepted by the community in which we all live
- to be able to choose how to lead individual lives and lifestyles.

Taken from www.asist.co.uk

The sexual rights of people with learning disabilities

The sexual rights of people with learning disabilities should be recognised and respected as part of their wholeness as human beings. Given this we must face the question of how we accomplish this.

A starting point for this type of work involves looking at people's rights.

It was acknowledged that upholding the basic human right of a person with a learning disability to exist as a sexual being must be coupled with risk assessment. The protection of vulnerable people is crucial and their welfare must be considered at all times. This means that to some extent privacy for the service user may need to be sacrificed if their sexual rights are to be upheld.

The following list, adapted from Fairbairn, Rowley and Bowen (1995), does not therefore advocate a universal application of rights for all; in appropriate situations the rights of people with a learning disability can include:

- **The right to be informed about sexuality and its place in human life, at times and at a level that allows this area of human being and experience to be as positive as possible.**
  Those working with service users will be best placed to decide what information each individual in their care is ready to assimilate and what it is necessary for them to know.

- **The same right as everyone else to enjoy sexual activity. The right to remain celibate and to refrain from sexual activity of any kind.**
  The same restrictions that the law places on everyone regarding sexual activity should also apply to service users. Sexual activity should not occur in places that may offend people or be abusive. Nor should there be an expectation that people with learning disabilities MUST engage in sexual activity or have any more right than anyone else to have sexual relationships.

- **The right to contraceptive advice and services both to avoid pregnancy and to avoid the risks of STIs.**
  There is no suggestion that it is right to impose methods of contraception onto someone because others believe that it is necessary to do so. However, protection from pregnancy and/or infection can be dealt with via preventative educational work.

- **The same right as any other citizen to marry or form ongoing sexual relationships.**
  This only applies where the person who wishes to marry is looking to marry someone who wishes to marry them or form a sexual relationship with them.

- **The same right to choose parenthood that is enjoyed by everyone else.**
  There should be no restrictions to this for people with learning disabilities and where appropriate they should be helped to develop necessary parenting skills. In situations where babies may be taken into public care or there are potential genetic issues, counselling and education should be provided. There is also a right to choose to avoid parenthood, including the right to abortion.

- **The right not to be sexually abused and to be protected from sexual abuse.**
  In a society where people with learning disabilities are so commonly devalued, it is important to reiterate this basic right and make explicit the behaviour that could constitute even mild abuse. Protection can also mean that individuals are empowered through education to seek help and say no if coerced into activities they do not like.

"It is not easy to relate theory to practice, but as carers, we have a duty to care for and promote individuals' rights."

RELEVANT RESOURCES

- *Your rights about sex* McCarthy and Cambridge, 1996.

- *The sexuality and sexual rights of people with learning disabilities: considerations for staff and carers* Cambridge, 1996.

  Both these publications are available from BILD Publications tel 01752 202301 and set out the rights and responsibilities in a very clear way.

- *Sexuality, learning disability and doing what's right* Fairbairn, Rowley and Bowen, 1995.

  David Fulton Publishers, available from bookshops.

- *Sex and the 3 R's: rights, responsibilities and risks* McCarthy and Thompson, 1992.

  Available from Pavilion Publications tel 01273 623222.

  A sex education package for working with people with learning difficulties. Being reprinted in 2003, will be available from June.

The importance of sex and relationships education

When considering sex and relationships education a key issue that frequently arises is one of rights set against the protection of people with learning disabilities. Staff members' duty of care requires that these are balanced. An individual's capacity to understand, retain and apply information when making decisions about their sex and relationship choices, and giving or refusing consent to an act, must be clearly monitored by staff.

Comprehensive, relevant and appropriate education can reduce the risk of:

- inappropriate sexual behaviour

- self injuries and/or violent behaviour caused by sexual frustration

- sexual abuse of or by others

- sexual activity unprotected against pregnancy and infection

- ignorance about their bodies

- lack of freedom and access to meet people, socialise and develop relationships

- difficulties in developing self-esteem and sexual self-image.

Valuing People

Valuing People: a new strategy for learning disabilities for the 21st century is a White Paper introduced by the Government in 2001.

The four key principles underpinning the White Paper are:

Legal and civil rights: people with learning disabilities have the right to a decent education, to grow up, to vote, to marry and have a family, to express opinions, with support as necessary.

Independence: the starting presumption should be of independence, rather than dependence, with public services providing the support needed to maximise this.

Choice: like other people, people with learning disabilities want a real say in where they live, what work they should do and who looks after them.

Inclusion: this means enabling people with learning disabilities to carry out day-to-day activities, make use of mainstream services and be fully included in local communities.

The implications of this for staff working with people with learning disabilities points to providing opportunities for their service users to gain information about contraception, sexually transmitted infections, pregnancy, parenthood, sexual orientation and sexual activity. Staff will also need to help with the development of decision-making skills, understanding and using information, communicating about sex and relationships, including marriage and recognising and dealing with potentially abusive situations.

Of equal importance will be helping service users to work out their own attitudes and values relating to sexuality and relationships.

Valuing People explicitly acknowledges the importance of social relationships, including those of a physical and sexual nature. It states:

"It is important that people can receive accessible sex education and information about relationships and contraception."

RELEVANT RESOURCE

- *Valuing People* can be downloaded from the following website: www.doh.gov.uk/learningdisabilities/strategy.htm along with an accessible version.

It can also be obtained from Department of Health Publications, PO Box 777, London, SE1 6XH, fax 01623 724524, e-mail doh@prolog.uk.com

Quote reference 23640 when ordering.

What did the training aim to do?

The three-day course was a mixture of formal information-giving and experiential learning using a participatory approach based on the course objectives.

The aim of the training:

- to improve awareness, skills and confidence in working more effectively in the area of sexuality and relationships with people with learning disabilities

This was achieved by:

- providing information about laws and policies that led to a clearer rationale for working with service users, parents, carers and other staff
- creating an understanding of values and attitudes (participants' own and other people's) to sexuality and how these impact on everyday practice
- providing information about contraception and sexually transmitted infections to promote the sexual well-being of clients
- offering an opportunity to experience practical, relevant communication skills to enhance sexual health, sexuality, sex and relationships work
- promoting recognition of the participants' own boundaries.

Sexuality

S exuality is an area of life that is fundamental to all people and is expressed everyday through beliefs, perception of selves as well as actions and communication with others.

"I have learnt that I have not incorporated 'sexuality' as part of the people I support and allowed them to explore their sexuality."

Clarifying what sexuality means is an essential part of reducing misunderstanding and fears held by some staff and parents who may be opposed to engaging with this area of work. Participants agreed that sexuality encompasses the spiritual, political, emotional, physical (including the sensual) and intellectual dimensions of a person's identity. This broad definition enables people with severe learning disabilities to access most aspects of this work.

When asked to focus on this wide definition of sexuality, the following ideas were produced:

When asked to put forward a definition of sexuality as they understood it staff devised the following:

Sexuality is ...

... an outward expression of sensual being and feelings, governed by both innate and environmental influences which is projected in personality and behaviour

... freedom to express individuality which defines essence, gender and personality

... an evolving and changing expression of self-identity to sustain or gain emotional and physical well-being through projection of self to others and their acceptance of your self

... a developing process throughout life of expressing your own identity, your SELF, through your attitudes and the attitudes of others

... an expression of self, to self and others, which is influenced by a combination of biological instinct, cultural and personal experiences and psychological development which changes and progresses through life

... a personal expression of an individual's masculinity or femininity based on behaviour, lifestyle choices, experiences and the way they choose to present themselves in society

... an individual's right to be able to express themselves spiritually, physically, intellectually, emotionally and socially without fear or prejudice

... a lifelong journey of self-discovery developing and understanding physical/psychological and spiritual needs. It is a discovery of who we are attracted to at various levels and learning from experiences to appropriate strategies towards fulfilment

Human sexuality includes, but is not limited to, the mechanics of sex and sexual orientation. It equally embodies everything about who we are, how we interact with the world, and how we deal with the impact that the world has upon us. Service users need to be supported in exploring these themes in a way that recognises their individual needs.

Spheres of influence

Wider society's perceptions of people with learning disabilities including discrimination, ignorance, exploitation and abuse

parents and carers

laws, policy and guidance

staff

person with learning disability

Where can we as professionals effect change?

When working with people with learning disabilities it is always useful to be aware of the influences which affect their life experiences. Unlike their non-disabled peers many people with learning disabilities will not have access to extensive social opportunities. Most of their learning will have come from a smaller network of people, parents/carers and staff from a wide variety of services, health and social care, education, day care and ancillary services.

Messages about friendships, relationships and sexuality may be omitted or filtered through a sincere desire to protect individuals from exploitation and abuse. Therefore it is necessary to acknowledge that the inner sphere of influence may be limited by this intention and recognise the impact that this will have on the service user's choices.

The outer sphere of influence represents society's exclusion of any disability. Staff do not have control over this outer sphere to tackle discrimination faced by those with a learning disability. Therefore staff should look to work within the inner sphere to develop consistent skills and awareness with service users which will uphold their rights and fulfil their duty of care. Working with service users to create a map of key people, institutions and rules which influence their lives can focus attention on creating a fully enabling environment to work in. It also serves to create a manageable challenge for staff which in turn can lead to the support and implementation of national policy to challenge wider societal perceptions.

The worker as a resource

The most important resources for effective sexuality work are skilled, supported and well-trained staff and carers. The training provided opportunities for participants to identify their professional needs and build their knowledge, confidence and skills.

Using the following model is a way of reflecting on the key areas that anyone involved in sexuality work needs to explore for themselves and the people they work with. During the training it helped participants recognise that in doing work based on life skills, empowerment and self-esteem that they are already doing sexuality work. It also highlighted the specific knowledge, awareness and skills that they need to work more pro-actively.

Sex and relationships work
The key elements

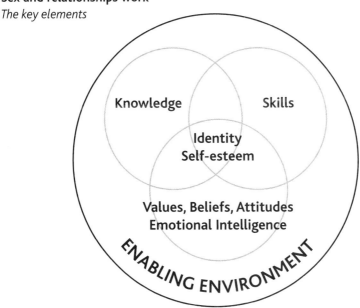

Issues and concerns for staff

Staff discussed their issues and concerns when supporting service users with sex and relationships, sexuality and sexual health education. Similar needs shared by staff around the country fell into the following categories:

Information

- the law
- consent – who can and cannot give it
- professional boundaries
- rights and responsibilities of service users, parents and staff
- national and local policy as well as guidance
- what constitutes abuse eg if teaching about masturbation
- contraception and safer sex.

Awareness and understanding

- personal values, beliefs and attitudes about sexuality
- diversity of perspectives on sexuality
- protection and rights
- discrimination faced by people with learning disabilities.

Skills

- more confidence in talking about sex, relationships, sexuality and sexual health
- delivering more proactive sexuality work
- communicating about the importance of this work to service users, their parents and carers, and colleagues
- getting training and support needs met.

The next sections expand upon these three areas, and describe how staff addressed them during the training.

Information

SEX AND THE LAW

Sex and the law is often one of the most confusing areas with the most inaccessible sources of information for staff. It is essential to have up-to-date facts about the law and also to know where to get more information.

People with learning disabilities have the same rights and responsibilities in law as any other person. Exclusions may apply to people with severe learning disabilities who are deemed unable to give consent in law. Their rights are not automatically transferred to parents or carers. In consultation with a range of professionals they may decide what is in the best interests of the service user.

> "The legal position relating to sexual behaviour is one of the key areas of uncertainty. Staff often do not know what the law is, and when the law has been considered, it leaves many areas of uncertainty."
>
> Sex and the Law, Gunn, **fpa** 1996.

There are 15 Acts which are directly relevant to the sexual behaviour and/or education of people with learning disabilities.

i) **Sexual Offences Act 1956**
   This deals, amongst other things, with the age of consent for heterosexual relationships; sexual intercourse with a 'defective' and indecent assaults committed on either men or women.

ii) **Mental Health Act 1959**
   Most of this Act has been superseded by the Mental Health Act 1983. However Section 128 dealing with sexual relationships between staff and 'patients' remains.

iii) **Sexual Offences Act 1967**
   Deals with male homosexuality and includes specific reference to males who have 'severe mental handicap'.

iv) Mental Health (Amendment) Act 1982

Updated parts of the Sexual Offences Acts 1956 and 1967 and the Mental Health Act 1959. Most of it has now been superseded by the Mental Health Act 1983. The amended definition of 'defective' and 'severe mental handicap' in the sexual offences legislation originates from this Act.

v) Mental Health Act 1983

Draws together provisions of the Mental Health Act 1959 and the Mental Health (Amendment) Act 1982 and supersedes most of those two.

vi) Sexual Offences Act 1985

Made changes in the sentences for certain offences. In particular it made the maximum punishment for indecent assault the same whether it is committed on a man or on a woman.

vii) Education (No.2) Act 1986

Added a provision about sex education in county, voluntary and special schools maintained by the local authority stating that in such schools sex education should 'encourage pupils to have due regard to moral considerations and the value of family life'.

viii) Local Government Act 1988

Introduced a new provision into an existing statute. This provision stated that local authorities must not expend finance so as intentionally 'to promote homosexuality or publish material with the intention of promoting homosexuality'.

Scotland repealed this provision in June 2000 saying:

"... this piece of legislation was, and remains, ill-conceived. Its existence has: served to legitimise intolerance and prejudice and, arguably, raised the level of homophobia ..."

England and Wales repealed the provision in July 2003, saying:

"Section 28 is about trying to use the law to embody their own prejudices. Section 28 has no place in the protection of children, let alone in a modern, civilised society."

ix) Sexual Offences Act 1993

Abolished the presumption that a boy under the age of 14 could not have sexual intercourse.

x) **Education Act 1993**
Introduced a number of important changes in relation to sex education in schools, including teaching around HIV and STIs and the exemption of children from aspects of sex education except biological.

xi) **Criminal Justice and Public Order Act 1994**
Introduced significant changes including acknowledging anal rape, rape within marriage and lowering the age of homosexual consent to 18.

xii) **Education Act 1996**
Made reference to sex education provision for 'special' schools.

xiii) **Learning and Skills Act 2000**
Made amendments to the Education Act 1996 as regards sex education provision for 'special' schools.

xiv) **Local Government Act 2000**
Added a clause regarding Section 28 and homophobic bullying.

xv) **Sexual Offences (Amendment) Act 2000**
Equalised the age of homosexual consent to 16 and introduced new 'abuse of a position of trust' offences.

"All legal issues have been cleared up for me."

WEB WATCH

Good websites for information about offences and Bills and Acts which have been passed or are being addressed include:

● *The new Sexual Offences Bill:*
www.publications.parliament.uk/pa/ld200203/ldbills/026/2003026.htm

● *All acts from 1988 passed through UK Parliament:*
www.legislation.hmso.gov.uk/acts.htm

● *General legal information:*
www.lawsociety.org.uk

Consent

Consent and capacity to consent is often one of the most challenging areas when considering sexual offences and how they relate to people with learning disabilities.

Present law states that someone who is legally termed as 'defective' or has a 'severe mental handicap' is deemed to not have the capacity to consent. The definition of these two descriptions is:

> "a state of arrested or incomplete development of mind which includes severe impairment of intelligence and social functioning."
>
> **Sex and the Law, Gunn, fpa** 1996

This classification for someone with a learning disability will have a significant impact on their freedom of sexual expression as 'defectives' have no legal rights to sexual activity at present.

As a rough guide, severe impairment of intelligence is often taken to mean those with an IQ below 50. However, with any classification several other factors, such as the client's social functioning, need to be taken into account.

The BMA and Law Society guidelines deal with the common law test of capacity to consent to sexual relations in that the person:

a) must be capable of understanding what is proposed and its implications

b) must be able to exercise choice (it is important to consider whether one party is in a position of power, which will influence the ability of the other party to consent).

The law at present *(July 2003)*

At present the sexual offences laws are:

> "a patchwork quilt of provisions ancient and modern that works because people make it do so, not because there is coherence and structure."
>
> **Setting the Boundaries. Home Office, July 2000**

Current law regarding indecent assault on a woman carries a maximum sentence of 10 years, as opposed to the same offence against a woman with learning disabilities which carries a maximum sentence of two years.

It is clear that there are issues which need revising and updating. The Home Office and Government recognises the need for reform in this area and they are reviewing the sex offences and sentencing. This will include a review of consent and capacity to consent.

DID YOU KNOW...

The sexual offences bill is before parliament at present (July 2003).
It aims to change many of the laws relating to people with learning
disabilities and sexual activity. The clauses which are directly relevant
are as follows:

Clauses 18 to 27
Offences related to abuse of a position of trust

Clauses 33 to 37
Offences against people with mental disorders or learning disabilities

Clauses 38 to 42
Inducements to people with mental disorders or learning disabilities

Clauses 43 to 51
Care workers for people with mental disorders or learning disabilities

Changes in the laws are expected in 2003.

RELEVANT RESOURCES – THE LAW

- *Sex and the law, a brief guide for staff working with people with
learning disabilities* MJ Gunn, **fpa**, 1996.

  *This publication is currently out of print but is still worth referring to as it is
  the most common for staff to use (ask your local health promotion agency).
  An updated version is being looked at when the sexual offences laws change.*

- *Easy guide to the Human Rights Act* Hughes and Coombs, 1998.

  *Available from: BILD Publications tel 01752 202301
  www.bild.org.uk/publications
  Outlines the key elements of the Act and shows how they can be applied to
  protect the legal rights of people with learning disabilities.*

POLICY AND GUIDANCE

Every organisation should have in place a policy and guidelines for staff working with adults with learning disabilities regarding personal and social relationships before any form of sexuality work is introduced.

During policy development everyone has a responsibility to respect the rights of others to freedom and choice. Staff must respect the rights and explain the responsibilities of people with learning disabilities whilst ensuring that they are not open to abuse or exploitation.

As with legal issues, people with severe learning disabilities will differ in their rights and responsibilities.

The rights of adults with learning disabilities include:

- access to guidance which will assist them in their social, personal and sexual development
- access to support and advice from people who are competent to provide it
- the opportunity to develop close, intimate and loving relationships and the privacy which this demands
- to have appropriate support and protection from exploitation, abuse and degrading treatment
- to have information about himself/herself kept confidential.

The responsibilities of adults with learning disabilities include:

- to stay within the law as any other citizen
- to respect the rights of others
- to treat others with respect, consideration and sensitivity.

The rights of carers/relatives include:

- to be clear about their role and the support available to them
- to be informed and consulted if the adult with learning disabilities has clearly expressed this as their wish
- to have appropriate support and protection from exploitation, abuse and degrading treatment that may be perpetrated by the people they care for

- to be treated with respect, consideration and sensitivity
- not to be held responsible for the action of the adult with learning disabilities.

The responsibilities of carers/relatives include:

- to work constructively with others involved in supporting the adult with learning disabilities as agreed in the care plan or any other agreement
- to treat their relative/adult with respect and consideration
- to make a distinction between what is in the best interest of their relative/person with a learning disability and what is in their own best interest
- to support and promote positive sexual health and relationships for the adult with learning disabilities and to respect their relationship choices and preferences
- to keep the services supporting them informed where appropriate.

The rights of staff and managers include:

- to have appropriate support and protection from exploitation, abuse and degrading treatment which may be perpetrated by the service users that they work with
- to be given relevant information, advice, support, supervision, and training from someone who is appropriately skilled and conversant with policy on personal and social relationships
- to be treated with respect, consideration and sensitivity
- to be protected from unfair allegations and adverse publicity and supported when allegations are made by means of policies and procedures.

The responsibilities of staff and managers include:

- to work constructively with others within policies and procedures to support adults with learning disabilities in pursuing personal and social relationships
- to report any incidents of abuse, neglect or poor practice in line with their employers' adult protection procedures in a non-judgemental manner
- To request training, support and guidance where necessary
- to ensure that the adult with learning disabilities is kept informed and treated with respect and dignity and appropriate confidentiality in a non-abusive, non-judgemental environment.

RELEVANT RESOURCES

- *Social and personal relationships – policy and good practice guidelines for staff working with adults with learning disabilities*
  by BILD and The West Midlands Learning Disability Forum.

  You can get this publication from BILD Publications tel 01752 202301.

  This publication aims to give a policy framework and provide guidance on how a policy can be used in different situations. This provides a good starting point for anyone wanting to put a policy together.

"I feel more confident and secure in my role and feel I will be able to help write a policy."

Local dilemmas: a practical approach

Policy and guidance are usually devised to not only reflect the law and national policy but also to respond to local dilemmas. Consultation with service users, other staff, parents and carers is at the heart of effective policy development. It enables all parties to own and endorse the work if they trust the process. It helps everyone agree their rights and responsibilities.

The statements used in training were intended to highlight the need for constructive debate and demonstrate how people might arrive at consensus. The concept of explicitly describing the different contexts that these statements could relate to meant that in using this process very specific local guidance points, within a policy, could be agreed upon and formulated.

Remember these statements are designed to provoke debate and are not recommendations of what should be put into practice.

STATEMENT 1:
Allowing mild unwanted sexual advances between service users enables the recipient the opportunity to learn the skill of assertiveness.

The spectrum of opinion ranged from:

- this is completely unacceptable, any form of sexual advance that is unwanted should be dealt with by staff

- empowerment requires skills to be practised. If a service user were taught the skill of assertiveness and expressed a desire to deal with the unwanted advances it would require staff support. Risk-taking in a controlled environment may be preferable to 'throwing people in at the deep end' unsupervised.

STATEMENT 2:
It is useful to discourage intimate relationships between service users when it is evident to staff that there is no long-term future for the couple.

Participant opinion:

- all service users have the same right to be in a relationship with few long-term possibilities as anyone else. Safeguards would come in the form of staff checking out that there is no exploitation or abuse in the situation.

STATEMENT 3:
Pornography is an acceptable form of personal relationships and sexuality education for service users.

The spectrum of opinion ranged from:

- pornography can show women and men in submissive and objectified roles and can give a negative message

- pornography is a choice that can be respected with safeguards, namely that staff do not provide pornography but support its use by explaining that it can only be used in a private space. An example offered was of a service user having satellite television in his bedroom that was monitored by staff in terms of agreed times for watching pornography. He also agreed to participate in other activities during the day

- proactive discussions about women and getting consent for sex would need to occur as part of a programme of sex and relationships education.

STATEMENT 4:
If service users are influenced by limiting parental values and beliefs about sexuality, it becomes the responsibility of staff to provide more diverse perspectives.

The spectrum of opinion ranged from:

- we need to work with parents to explain the benefits of sex and relationships work and the rights of the service user

- service users often visit or live with their parents so any new skills, awareness or information that staff provide needs to recognise the context in which people live or return to regularly

- providing 'diverse perspectives' is useful only if it is tailored to the individual. So if exactly the same information is given to all service users it could equally prove destructive if it is not appropriate to their needs.

STATEMENT 5:
Demonstrations of affection between service users of the same sex are less acceptable in public than service users of the opposite sex

The spectrum of opinion ranged from:

- the rights of people of every sexual orientation to express affection must be supported

- the law and society still discriminates against people who are gay showing affection in public, so teaching service users this fact and the reality of discrimination is necessary for their protection.

STATEMENT 6:
All service users, regardless of sexual orientation, require information about marriage, pregnancy and parenthood

Participant opinion:

- all service users need this information even if they never experience first hand any of these situations.

STATEMENT 7:
Service users should always be encouraged, by staff, to explore their sexual needs and feelings

The spectrum of opinion ranged from:

- some service users might just want a special friend without wanting to become sexually intimate with them

- while exploring sexual needs and feelings could be encouraged it should not **always** have to happen, only when appropriate

- it is vital for some service users as their aggressive behaviour has been shown to decline when educated about dealing with sexual frustration.

STATEMENT 8:
All service users need to be informed of the variety of behaviours that constitute sexual abuse

The spectrum of opinion ranged from:

- talking about it to all service users might scare some of them

- you must be prepared with an agreed process or plan if someone discloses that they are being or have been abused

- there needs to be a programme developed to inform service users of what are appropriate behaviours from a range of people involved in their lives

- this must be coupled with assertiveness work eg expressing (verbally or otherwise) "no" to unwanted touches or anything they are not sure of and stating what they want until they are able to talk to a trusted person.

STATEMENT 9:
Masturbation in a public part of the house can be tolerated if no other service user is there, or likely to be present

Participants' opinions

- this must be discouraged as it gives a mixed message about public places

- masturbation in private should be discussed and enabled where necessary.

■■■■■■■■■ top tip ■■■■■■■■■

There are organisations and people who can help you with your policy development such as **fpa**, ARC (Association of Residential Care) or BILD (British Institute of Learning Disabilities).

fpa can provide training in sexuality policies. Contact the training department on 020 7923 5232.

Accessible policies for service users

Policies have a major impact on the opportunities and experiences of the service user. They should be adapted and written in an accessible way which can be understood and used by people with learning disabilities.

■■■■■■■■■ **top tip** ■■■■■■■■■

An extremely good example of this is a policy produced by Yarrow Housing Ltd, written by Image in Action. They have two separate documents, one entitled *The sexuality of people with learning disabilities: policy and guidelines* **for general distribution, and one entitled** *Let's talk about sex – your sexuality, rights and how Yarrow can help you* **for service users.**

You can get both publications for £10 from Yarrow Housing Ltd, 216 Goldhawk Road, London W12 9NX, tel 020 8740 4735, e-mail info@yarrowhousing.org.uk.

CONTRACEPTION AND SEXUALLY TRANSMITTED INFECTIONS

While staff reported that many service users do not use contraceptives, some highlighted that the most common forms of contraception often centred on sterilisation for men and women, the pill and the hormonal injection.

Male condom use for safer sex was the main contraceptive method promoted by staff. Time was spent on giving information about the different forms of contraception and sexually transmitted infections which gave participants the opportunity to look at the options and risks that service users could be enabled to explore with staff. It helped to clarify professional boundaries in terms of giving information or being advocates when referring service users to a health professional.

■■■■■■■■■■ top tip ■■■■■■■■■■

Some special schools in Tower Hamlets have mock family planning clinics so pupils can practice going to a clinic and asking for what they want. These mock clinic sessions are followed up by an accompanied trip to an actual clinic. Taking service users to a clinic and supporting them through a first visit can demystify the process and make it easier for them to go again. They can also help to support other service users as peer recommendation can be very powerful.

For a list of local clinics visit www.fpa.org.uk or phone Sexual Health Direct on 0845 310 1334.

DID YOU KNOW...

At present there are many forms of contraception available, all of which are highly efficient if used according to instructions. They are: Injection, Implant, Intrauterine System (IUS), Intrauterine Device (IUD), Female Sterilisation, Male Sterilisation, Combined Pill, Progestogen-only Pill (POP), Male Condom, Female Condom (Femidom), Diaphragms or Caps, Contraceptive Patch, Natural Family Planning, Emergency Contraception.

Condoms (male and female), if taught and used correctly, are the only methods of contraception that will provide protection from many, although not all, sexually transmitted infections.

There are issues around consent and contraception and many staff indicated situations within the workplace where the reasons that a service user was using contraception were unclear. This is an unsatisfactory situation which should be addressed within the policies and guidelines of the organisation whilst maintaining a person-centred approach.

WEB WATCH

Some good websites for information on contraception and sexually transmitted infections are:

- *fpa*   www.fpa.org.uk
- *Brook*   www.brook.org.uk
- *Marie Stopes International*   www.likeitis.org.uk

■■■■■■■■■ top tip ■■■■■■■■■

How could you describe the way hormonal contraception works to someone with a learning disability? To visually explain the release of progestogen or oestrogen into the body try dissolving a soluble aspirin in water and discuss how hormones release periodically.

RELEVANT RESOURCE

fpa produces a range of contraception leaflets dealing with all of the above methods. Small quantities of each leaflet are available free from your local health promotion unit. Extra copies can be ordered from **fpa direct** tel 01865 719418.

"I have learnt more about the individual nature of my work as regards contraception. I will aim to liaise with other professionals more regarding sexual health."

Awareness and understanding

DISCRIMINATION

Idiots, feeble-minded, natural fools, lunatic, imbeciles, mentally deficient, morally defective, mentally defective, are just some of the names that have appeared in legislation, dating back to the 14th century, that describe people with learning disabilities. The idea that people from these groups were 'highly prolific' and had 'problems of delinquency and alcoholism' was the subject of public debate in the early 20th century. It was concluded that people with a learning disability should be segregated from the general population. Later the idea of sterilisation to prevent these devalued and 'ineducable' citizens from reproducing was considered acceptable.

> "In a group I run ... it took the men some months to talk about their disability, within a session where they revealed the many labels that had been attached to them, such as mongol, idiot and spastic, labels which had been readily internalised. In a number of sessions the men have taken time to explore the reality of their births, describing themselves as 'coming out of mum all wrong'."
>
> **Young People, Learning Disabilities and Sexuality, www.respond.org.uk, March 2000**

Public policy has come a long way from this historical position of accepted discrimination, introducing the philosophies of social role valorisation and normalisation to other initiatives such as care in the community and, more recently, the White Paper *Valuing People*. However, in general, society still devalues and discriminates against people with learning disabilities and sexuality is a prime area to deny individuals their rights to exist as a whole person.

People may face multiple discrimination if they are from a particular ethnic or cultural community, religious background or class, or if they define themselves as lesbian, gay or bisexual.

> "The sex life and sexuality of people with a learning disability is often ignored or dismissed ... Add to that the further difficulties of being gay and you have the potential for severe isolation, loneliness and further mental health issues."
>
> **Meeting the needs of gay men with learning difficulties, Fox, Lesbian and Gay Foundation, 2002**

Staff should be working in an anti-discriminatory way in all areas of work and for all service users. Staff need to understand the social, ethnic and cultural backgrounds that service users originate from and whether they wish to retain or change these influences. Part of staff members' professional role is to provide experiences and opportunities that are inclusive of diversity for all service users. It is also to challenge discrimination whenever appropriate in local communities and promote positive images of people with learning disabilities.

Anti-discriminatory practice

Formulating working agreements is the cornerstone of developing anti-discriminatory practice when working with individuals or groups of people with learning disabilities, other staff members or parents and carers. These help make explicit how people should treat each other and expect to be treated. The individual or group can therefore feel valued and heard within an inclusive environment.

Participants from Taunton devised some working agreements which could be used for individuals or groups of people with learning disabilities. The following suggestions are taken from their work.

Working agreements/ground rules for service users

- information about you belongs to you. It is your choice who you tell
- information about other people belongs to them. It is their choice who they tell
- we will try to use language we can all understand so choose your own words
- if you don't understand anything ASK

- it is helpful if you are able to say, able to show, sign, draw ...

  "I think..."

  "I feel..."

  "I want..."

  "I like..."

  "I don't like..."

"I have learnt how to evaluate my own beliefs and values and how to put these aside and work in an open minded manner."

- what you say to us is private unless you or someone else might not be safe. I will tell you first if I think I need to talk to someone else, I will be honest with you

- we might not always agree – people think different things and that is OK

- we will try to make a safe space.

SEXUAL MESSAGES: PERSONAL INSIGHT AND PROFESSIONAL PRACTICE

What we learn and absorb about sexuality as we are growing up affects our lives and actions. Information about gender, puberty, friendships, relationships, sexual activity or sexual orientation can come from a range of both reliable and unreliable sources. Reflecting on personal experiences of growing up must be tempered with a recognition that everyone's childhood may not have been ideal. However in looking back staff explored how they received their sexual messages and the effect these have had on their adult lives.

Comparing their experiences with those of the people they work with enabled staff to consider the often negative, or missing, messages which people with learning disabilities receive about sexuality. This can have a huge impact on the way a service user views themselves.

"I have learnt that I make assumptions based on my own beliefs and messages."

This area provoked a great deal of discussion. A cross section of key points from staff members' personal experiences coupled with observations about service users' experiences are described below.

Parents/carers have a powerful influence on how anyone views themselves as a sexual person. The approach of the participants' own parents varied enormously depending on how they were brought up and their values and attitudes, but also from generation to generation. Parents of people with learning disabilities often find this concept very challenging.

> *"The parents I deal with in my work are often of an older generation. They are struggling to deal with some of the more modern ways of thinking, never mind accepting that their 40-year-old daughter with a learning disability may have a right to be sexual – they do not deal with this area, that is a powerful message in itself."*

Friends/peers also send powerful messages. A lot of information is also picked up at school. The information can be drawn from myths and second hand gossip, or can be from personal experience. It may be sensationalised and very subjective. Taking all of these things into account, friends/peers represent a main factor in learning about sexual activity and behaviour. Even if the 'information' is inaccurate or unreliable, it is powerfully influential.

> *"Very few of the clients I work with have equal peer friendships and it is very difficult to promote this. I think they miss out on getting messages from friends and those they do get are often not factual."*

Sex and relationships education (SRE) again varied greatly depending on the age of staff and where they went to school. Some experienced very well structured, planned, thorough sessions, others remembered SRE as being one half-day lesson. Ethnic, religious or cultural influences also had a significant effect on what participants learned about acceptable behaviours and identities.

"One of my students was taken out of his SRE session at his mainstream school last week and was made to do other work instead as it was deemed he would not understand. What sort of message is that giving?"

The media was cited as having an extensive influence on the messages staff receive. We are bombarded with sexual messages from television, magazines (including pornography), newspapers and books. This can have an impact on our relationship expectations, self-confidence and self-esteem as well as causing confusion by sending people very mixed messages.

"The positive representation of people with learning disabilities in the media is practically non-existent but the media plays such a powerful part in their lives. It is worrying that service users can be so involved in a soap opera like 'Eastenders' and possibly be unable to distinguish that from reality. We need to think about the type of messages soaps give."

Personal experience helped many staff to form opinions, make decisions and gain knowledge. Even when the experiences were negative they gave valuable messages.

"Service users often lack the opportunity to gain personal experience and learn through relationships going well or badly. There is not enough scope to let people with learning disabilities make their own mistakes, it's seen as too big a risk to take."

POSITIVE SEXUALITY: WHAT CAN WE PROVIDE?

"I have learnt that everybody has a right to have a positive sexuality and be helped (if required) to express themselves."

Due to the missing or often negative messages people with learning disabilities receive about their sexuality staff have a duty of care to look at how to positively promote sexuality. Unpicking what anyone needs for a positive sexuality in terms of information, skills and awareness can help staff to consider what areas of work they could develop for their service users.

These were some ideas from participants.

The group was asked:

● *What does anyone need for a positive sexuality?*

No guilt

Confidence

Feeling attractive

Self-worth

Good role models

Self-awareness

Empowerment

Positive parental messages

Positive feedback

Choice

Privacy

Safe environment for experiences

Network of resources/people

Awareness of emotions

Value of self and being valued

Education

Self-respect

Freedom of expression

Sexual relationship

Trust

And ...

- *What messages can we give to promote this?*

Empowerment

It's normal!   Promotion of gender identity

Religious/cultural issues   Openness

Diversity is positive

Good to feel positively sexual   Honesty

Sex is natural

Understanding of the law   Positive self-image

Respect

Good self-esteem

Value   Everyone is different

Honouring people's choices

Equality within relationships

Accepting that most of these needs and messages were unavailable to the service users they worked with the group was then asked:

- *What can you do in your current role to change this?*

Training for staff (supported by management and other staff)
Promote a safe environment which includes:
— confidentiality
— being non-judgemental
Work with parents
See people as individuals, not as a condition or disability
Be aware of issues
Take calculated risks
Trust service users
REAL privacy
Positive encouragement
Promotion of BASIC HUMAN RIGHTS
Promotion of decision making – yes AND no
Offer informed choice
Be honest
Listen
Have the time to allow expression of emotion

WORKING WITH PARENTS AND CARERS

Working in partnership with parents and carers of service users is an essential aspect of the role of staff members. It is important to recognise that parental behaviours which are seen as restrictive will usually have the very positive intention of protection behind them. If staff acknowledge that fear and grief could lie behind a parent's protective impulse it may lead to better dialogue with parents and carers who are opposed to sexuality work.

"Bringing up a child who is not 'perfect' in the eyes of the world, often instigates a period of grieving for the 'lost child' ie the child you were expecting but did not have. How the diagnosis is given and the disability explained is crucial to how well parents are able to deal with this situation emotionally and intellectually.

Families who are unable to grieve can become stuck and this can block the idea that their child could ever reach any form of maturity. Expressions of grief may be felt throughout the whole of the child's life not just immediately after diagnosis.

Having the opportunity to express the sadness and the grief over not having the child expected can help parents to move forward. The more parents are able to come to terms with the disability of their son or daughter the more they may then be able to accept them as sexual beings."

Holding On, Letting Go, **Drury et al**

RELEVANT RESOURCES
BOOKS FOR PARENTS AND CARERS

- ***Holding on, letting go – sex, sexuality and people with learning disabilities*** John Drury, Lynne Hutchinson and Jon Wright, Souvenir Press, 2000.

    A book for parents and carers to help them feel more comfortable and confident when thinking about sex and sexuality in relation to their son, daughter or caree. Available from all bookshops.

- ***Talking together… about growing up*** Scott and Kerr-Edwards, **fpa**, 1999. **fpa direct**: PO Box 1078, E.Oxford DO, Oxon, OX4 5JE tel 01865 719418

    A workbook for parents of children with learning disabilities.

- ***Talking together… about sex and relationships*** Scott and Kerr-Edwards, **fpa**, 2003.

    *The second in the Talking together series for parents is also now available from **fpa direct**, as above.*

Rehearsing responses, parents and carers: a practical approach

Talking to parents and service users about their issues and concerns around sex and relationships was explored in a question and response session.

These questions explored:

- helping a son to masturbate

- a daughter's over-affectionate behaviour with strangers

- a son needing condoms

- fears that a son or daughter will be exposed to sexual activity

- concerns that a daughter is talking about getting married

- a daughter wanting to use tampons.

The discussion centred on what knowledge, skills and awareness staff need to respond positively to questions like these.

Parents and carers of service users may approach staff with fear, anxiety and mistrust based on past experiences where their sons and daughters may have been left open to exploitation or abuse. There may have been situations where staff ignored parental concerns because they did not feel equipped to deal with issues such as masturbation. A two-way discussion with parents and carers could use the following three levels of response:

1. **The emotional**
   listening to the emotional and sometimes irrational – allowing the parent to feel heard and understood

   Skills can include:

   - **empathy:** demonstrate that you are able to put yourself in their situation and view the issue as they do

   - **active listening:** using open questions widens the conversation and reflecting back what they have said can allow them to confirm that you have heard and understood their perspective

   - **honesty:** be realistic – do not be tempted to reassure if there is nothing concrete to back this up or if it will infringe the service users' rights

   - **clear communication with organisation:** ensure that you feel supported (by manager, colleagues, policy) to give information, advice and reassurance.

2. The rational
imparting information relevant to the situation

Information can include knowledge of:

- the law
- *Valuing People*
- local policies on equal opportunities and sexuality
- local and national guidelines and procedures
- professional boundaries
- duty of care
- rights and responsibilities of colleagues, parents/carers and service users.

3. Personal skills
using personal skills – enabling the parent to feel comfortable and accepted

Qualities can include:

- showing that you value the person
- understanding
- being non-judgemental
- not taking emotive actions personally
- not acting on assumptions but checking out what the parent means – misunderstandings can be destructive
- being honest so that trust can be built
- mediating difficult behaviours.

"I realised that I have personal feelings but to fulfil my role responsibly I must listen to all perspectives, from the client to their parents and other colleagues and be broadminded and empathetic."

WORKING WITH RELUCTANT COLLEAGUES

Staff highlighted that without clear guidance about professional boundaries for sex and relationships work with service users, many colleagues felt reluctant to engage in the debate, let alone the work itself.

Without policy or training some staff allowed their personal beliefs to dictate what they would or would not do with service users. While this is both potentially discriminatory and a failure to carry out their duty of care, tackling their reluctance without listening to their concerns and giving time for explanation was not considered to be a way forward.

As with any emotive situation, it is important that people's fear and anxiety is heard and responded to appropriately before a rational theory as to the benefits of sex and relationships work can be put forward.

Potential 'barriers' posed by reluctant staff

- *"Doing this work will put ideas into their heads, they only have the mental age of children so it would encourage them to have sex."*

  RESPONSES:

  Emotional: I can see you feel very strongly about this ... tell me about your concerns.

  Rational: Mental age does not necessarily have a bearing on someone's capacity to consent. People with learning disabilities should be enabled to enjoy their rights as individuals. They should be helped to make informed choices coupled with their right to protection and freedom from discrimination.

- *"It is against my religion to condone sex out of marriage, I would feel compromised."*

  RESPONSES:

  Emotional: Tell me about your religion ...

  Rational: Religions have set codes of conduct and they also usually have a pastoral brief to support individuals even if they have contravened the rules. In any work situation your personal attitudes cannot take precedence over your professional duty of care which may not conform to your personal beliefs. This kind of behaviour could be construed as discriminatory against the service user.

- **"The parents would not allow it."**

RESPONSES:

Emotional: What has been your experience of working with these parents? How do you feel about their behaviour?

Rational: Whose rights must we primarily uphold under the law? Our duty of care is to the service user but it would also include dialogues with parents/carers who hold a significant position of influence. We may as a staff group need to explore how we deal with the fear and grief that parents/carers may experience that hampers the development of this work.

- **"It's all very well to talk about their rights but we don't know the first thing about this work."**

RESPONSES:

Emotional: What do you think this work involves? What might you feel particularly uncomfortable talking about?

Rational: Describe what sex and relationships work involves eg life skills – you are already doing this and it is transferable. We will make sure you will have a policy and guidance that you can discuss and also that there is good quality training available – honest reassurance. Note: never bring reluctant colleagues into this work without a guarantee of policy, guidance and training.

- **"Some of them have been abused, we don't want to open a 'can of worms.'"**

RESPONSES:

Emotional: Tell me about the types of general behaviour people display who have been abused. How do you feel about dealing with that?

Rational: We will need to plan one-to-one work and general sex and relationships work that is distanced and practical eg exploring acceptable public and private behaviours, making decisions like saying no to unwanted attention, what consent means and how to seek advice.

- **"Some of them try to harass and abuse the others, talking about sex will just make it worse."**

RESPONSES:

Emotional: I understand and share your fears. If we do not tackle this appropriately it could prove more difficult.

Rational: Again we need to plan one-to-one work and general sex and relationships work that is distanced and practical eg exploring acceptable public and private behaviours, making decisions like saying no to unwanted attention, what consent means and how to seek help and advice.

- **"Are you saying we should encourage them to have sex, what if someone gets pregnant? I don't want to have to tell the parents."**

  RESPONSES:

  Emotional: I understand your reluctance to do this. Tell me what you think this work is about.

  Rational: Let me reassure you that doing this work is not about encouragement but meeting people's needs appropriately. We need to be prepared to give information about pregnancy, contraception and planning families. We also need to look at ideas for engaging parents in sex and relationships work and provide reassurance about the roles and responsibilities of the staff member.

- **"I don't want to get into talking about gay and lesbian stuff."**

  RESPONSES:

  Emotional: What are your concerns in discussing these issues?

  Rational: People have choices and offering the right amount of information about homosexuality at the right time can be empowering. Discussion around personal views and beliefs being imposed on service users is again about being discriminatory if personal attitudes override good professional practice and service users rights.

- **"I don't want to teach someone to masturbate."**

  RESPONSES:

  Emotional: What would most concern you if you were asked to do this?

  Rational: Not everyone would be expected to do this. There are many ways of teaching this that do not involve physical contact such as using line drawings or videos and talking it through. At the very least we would want all staff to support those who are teaching about masturbation by being positive if asked a question by service users even if you then pass them on to someone else.

- **"Why do I have to do it?"**

  RESPONSES:

  Emotional: What concerns you about having to take this on as part of your role?

  Rational: As before, it will include our duty of care, anti-discriminatory practice, offering informed choice and appropriately promoting the sexual rights of people with learning disabilities.

- **"Who or what will support me? Will I get training?"**

  Responses:

  Emotional: What support and training do you feel you would need? Who and what would you like to support you?

  Rational: As before – honest reassurance about policy, guidance, training, supervision and support.

Dealing with the emotional – fears and concerns – takes time and understanding. Some colleagues will never be convinced or feel able to support the work. In such cases staff described situations where people resigned rather than feel compromised to deliver education in this area. Acting with such integrity enables the sexual rights of service users to be upheld by staff whose skills lie in this area.

Skills

COMMUNICATION

Language and service users

The context of words and language is very important. A word used in a particular, possibly derogatory, manner may have a very different emphasis when being used between friends to express something.

"I have learnt about language that can be used to talk about sexuality with confidence."

Staff discussed the use of language as being one of the main areas of concern for them when working with people with learning disabilities. Groups established some ways of working from this which included:

● establish your levels of language when starting work with a group

● discuss all the words that can be used for different sexual activities and private body parts and come to a common consensus on what is acceptable

● make sure that the words you are using are understood by the group

● make sure you establish that the words the group use are what you interpret them to be

● the more you use a word, the less embarrassing it can become, try some exercises around making the words more everyday for people

● establish that the words which are used in the group may not be appropriate for use in situations outside the group

● make sure your working agreement (see page 32) has a point about appropriate language.

RELEVANT RESOURCE

● *A very touching book* by Jan Hindman is a good resource for looking at appropriate touch and has a great section addressing words and language and breaking down barriers with sexual language.

It's from the US – ISBN 0-9611034-1-8

Rehearsing responses, service users

Staff practised responses to service user questions that covered areas such as:

● marriage

● not enjoying sex

● touching parts of bodies

● thinking they were in love with the staff member

● pregnancy and having babies

● sharing a room with their partner.

"I have learnt about listening to service users when they want to say something to me."

In responding to service user questions staff identified similar qualities and skills needed when answering the parent/carer questions but felt that they needed much greater access to information and knowledge of services.

A programme of work

Of prime importance was discussion centring on useful areas of proactive sex and relationships work with service users. A programme of work could include:

Principles and values
Rights and responsibilities
The law
Consent and decision-making
Confidentiality
Self esteem and identity
Sexual activity
Friendships
Knowing your body
Public and private behaviours
Communication and assertiveness
Making your own decisions
Privacy
Boundaries
Safety
Personal relationships
Sex and relationships education
Sexual health
Sexual orientation
Masturbation
Contraception and sexually transmitted infections
Pregnancy and unplanned pregnancy and parenting
Marriage and other partnerships
Pornography
Abuse and exploitation

■■■■■■■■■ top tip ■■■■■■■■■

There is an advanced accredited training course which addresses putting together such a programme of work run by **fpa**:

● *Sex and relationships work in practice – working with people with learning disabilities*

For more details ring the training department on 020 7923 5232.

SKILLS TEACHING

The process of teaching a new skill to someone with a learning disability takes careful thought, planning and execution.

Staff looked at how to simplify language and instructions to explain a step by step process for one of the following:

> **Male/female condom use**
> **Sanitary towel use**
> **Tampon use**

Staff considered the information service users needed in addition to the 'how to'. Very few resources were provided so staff needed to be creative.

It would be very difficult to encapsulate all the presentations seen throughout the training. There were fantastic ideas, thoughts, models made and demonstrations given. Some groups chose to use pictures with verbal explanations, others added models and some demonstrated visually. A mixture of the groups' session ideas have been selected to structure this feedback.

"I have gained knowledge of the aspects of sexuality and the skills required for providing practical teaching."

These plans could be carried out over a series of weeks, not just in one session. Certain points may need repetition and further explanation.

Male condom use

1 *What is a condom?*

- show condoms in and out of packets

- explain where they can be obtained – eg bought from chemists or free from family planning clinics (accompany service user to these places the first time)

- explain what they do – prevent pregnancy and most sexually transmitted infections.

2 *When should they be used?*

- explain when – during sexual intercourse (vaginal, anal or oral) – put on just before penetration

- make this explicit – a male form of contraception for use on erect penis only.

3 Checking your condom

- talk about checking for date and kite mark/CE mark.

4 How to use

- how to open packet – no rings or sharp things, not with teeth
- how to ensure it is the right way up – see **top tips**
- how to roll condom onto the erect penis – demonstrate with model, remember holding the teat at the top of the condom to leave space for sperm
- when it is ok to have sex – when condom has rolled comfortably to end of erect penis.

5 Afterwards

- explain withdrawal – ensure condom is held securely at bottom
- explain removal – ensuring sperm in condom
- explain disposal – wrapped up in bin, not down toilet.

6 What if something goes wrong?

- discuss problems putting condoms on – use another, always make sure you have plenty
- discuss what to do if one splits or comes off – tell someone or go to family planning clinic or doctor
- only ever use a condom once.

top tips

One of the most difficult parts of this demonstration is explaining which way up the condom needs to go. Close your eyes and feel around the edges, when it is the right way up you can feel a textured edge and the wrong way is very smooth.

Make sure you have lots of condoms for the group to try with condom demonstrators and also some to take home if they want to try putting it on themselves.

Condom demonstrators are better to use than vegetables (less abstract) – you can get them for around £6 each from FP sales tel 01865 719400.

Female condom use

1 *What is a female condom?*

- show condoms in and out of packets

- explain where they can be bought from – chemists (may need to be ordered) some family planning clinics will provide them free of charge

- explain what they do – prevent pregnancy and sexually transmitted infections.

2 *When should it be used?*

- explain when – during vaginal intercourse

- make explicit – it is a female form of contraception for use in women only.

3 *Where is it used?*

- discuss female sexual organs – external and internal. Where the cervix is and how the female condom acts as a barrier there.

4 *How to use*

- how to open packet – no rings, sharp objects or with teeth

- what it feels like – very lubricated

- explain why it looks like it does – inner ring to sit against cervix, outer ring to stay outside vagina

- describe insertion (using model, visual diagrams)

- explain when it is ready to use – note that during sex the man's penis needs to be guided into the femidom to ensure it does not go outside it.

5 *Afterwards*

- removal – after the man has come the female condom must be removed by twisting the end to keep the sperm in and removing gently

- disposal – wrapped in tissue in the bin, not down the toilet.

"Learning how to handle a femidom without it 'getting away' will never be forgotten!"

▪▪▪▪▪▪▪▪▪▪ top tips ▪▪▪▪▪▪▪▪▪▪

Generally speaking it was agreed that the female condom would be a difficult form of contraception for a woman with a learning disability to use.

Working with women on the motor skills needed to use a female condom was looked at and doing some exercises around pinching and twisting were suggested.

Although we had some fantastic resources made for this section out of plastic cups and paper you can buy vaginal models for this type of work which may make things more visually comprehensive (good for tampon work too).

They can be bought from: FP sales tel 01865 719400.

Sanitary towel use (pads, pantyliners)

1 *Periods and when to use sanitary towels*

● talk about periods, monthly cycles, why sanitary towels are used and the different names for them.

2 *What are sanitary towels?*

● show different types of sanitary towel, different absorbencies, winged and non-winged

● Explain where to get them from (see **top tips**).

3 *How to use a sanitary towel*

● Explain process such as the following:

1 Go to toilet, this must be done in private

2 Wash hands, go into cubicle with sanitary towel

3 Take down lower garments and knickers

4 Sit on toilet and unwrap it (if it has a covering)

5 Take off strip of paper covering the sticky back and place sanitary towel onto gusset of knickers with sticky side down (this may need some practical help to ensure it is stuck in correct place – see **top tips**)

6 If it has wings, peel off the strips of paper fold under the gusset and stick down

7 Pull lower garments up

8 Wash hands.

4 *Changing and disposal*

- explain changing – that sanitary towels will need to be changed depending on the flow of your period and time of day

- explain disposal – sanitary towels need to be disposed of carefully – think about all the different situations clients may be in when changing their sanitary towel and explain that it should be as discreet as possible.

▪▪▪▪▪▪▪▪▪ top tip ▪▪▪▪▪▪▪▪▪

Staff spoke about making this work special for their female clients by bringing in make up bags and allowing the group to choose a pair of knickers and some sanitary towels to keep as their own.

The winged sanitary towels tend to be better for service users as they move around less – do some preliminary work on which side is sticky and where it should go – it is good to do this with actual knickers.

One staff member from Croydon had approached her local supermarket and asked if she could take a group in to shown them how the towels are packaged, what they cost, where to find them and what the different types are. Not only did this supermarket say yes they also offered an after hours session where the women could open the packets and see what they looked like inside.

Tampon use

1 *Periods and when to use tampons*

- talk about periods, monthly cycles and why tampons are used

- explain choice – why they are sometimes used instead of sanitary towels.

2 *What are tampons?*

- show different types of tampon, applicator and non-applicator and sizes

- describe where to get tampons from.

3 *How to use a tampon*

- describe process – see following visual presentation (pages 55–56).

4 *Changing and disposal*

- explain tampon changing – how often they should be changed.

  A suggested chart to give to clients so they can check they have changed their tampons:

	Getting Up	Lunchtime	Teatime	Bedtime
Day 1				
Day 2				
Day 3				
Day 4				
Day 5				

- explain disposal – in the bin wrapped in tissue, not down the toilet.

"I have much more confidence and experience of demonstration techniques."

Remember, some women with learning disabilities only ever use sanitary towels, not by choice, but because they have never been given another option. Tampons can provide an alternative option in suitable situations.

Be careful if using fake blood (or red water!) with tampon demonstrations, some women get very upset by this.

Do bear in mind associated health risks if tampons are not changed regularly, eg toxic shock syndrome. This will need to be dealt with carefully so as not to scare the client.

RELEVANT RESOURCE

● *Let's do it: creative activities for sex education for young people with learning disabilities* Johns, Scott and Bliss, 2002 (3rd edition).

Available from Image in Action: Resources, Image in Action, Chinnor Road, Bledlow Ridge, High Wycombe, Bucks HP14 4AJ tel 01494 481632.

For a good practical approach to sex education this publication includes activities that are drama-based or use visual images for use in schools, colleges and day centres.

Visual presentation

It was very hard to chose one particular visual presentation to put in here as so many were outstanding. One group in Cornwall made a booklet to explain tampon use which is incredibly simple, yet clear and concise. The following pages show the pictures and instructions from this.

How to use tampons

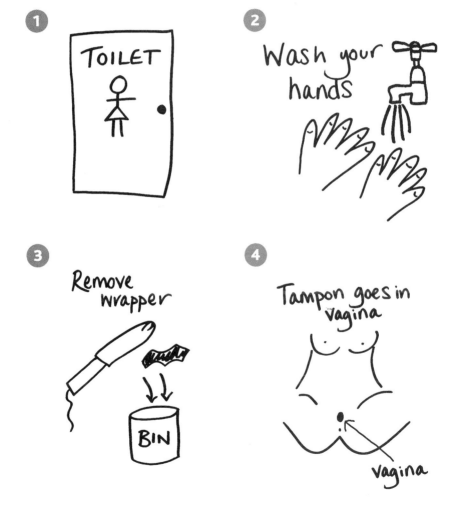

1 TOILET

2 Wash your hands

3 Remove wrapper — BIN

4 Tampon goes in vagina — vagina

5 Remove pants

+ Sit on toilet

6

1. Push tampon into vagina

2. Grip with other hand

3. Push with one finger

4. Pull both cardboard tubes out

7 String stays outside

Put tube in bin

BIN

8

Pull up knickers

and sort out clothes

9 Wash hands again

10 Change tampon every 4 hours

or if there is leaking on knickers

Conclusions

7

The Roadshow project provided essential training for staff working with people with learning disabilities which would not otherwise have been available to them.

With such demands on budgets, it is often fundamental areas of training, such as sexuality work, which are sacrificed for other issues, seen as more practical, or essential. The staff who attended the roadshows felt differently after the experience.

"This is such an essential area of work which I did not consider before, I now realise the importance of allowing service users to explore their sexuality."

In some areas of the country sexuality training is being introduced into induction programmes as a mandatory element. This is a very positive step forward for employers to be recognising the importance of this work and one which **fpa** fully supports.

Society Guardian was interested in the project and published an article on 9 April 2003 entitled 'Choice Matters' which highlighted some of the findings from the process.

"I think everyone who works in learning disabilities should do it!"

"... many staff on the courses felt unclear about what is and is not legal. Similarly there were concerns about employers policies and guidelines when it came to balancing the duty of care with respect for people's rights as sexual beings."

The courses aimed to break down some of these barriers and from the feedback we can see this was achieved.

Armed with the wealth of information and ideas encapsulated in this publication staff went away with plans to talk to their colleagues, to discuss and develop policy and to form networks for advice and support. This has developed over the months following the courses, with **fpa** seeing a surge in good practice around policy development across partnering organisations and very strong networks and alliances being formed.

We would like to applaud all the good examples of work being carried out around England as a result of the roadshow training and thank all the staff who attended the courses for their commitment, skill, passion and belief.

"I feel better able to support my clients in this area and confident to work with my manager to develop policies and procedures."

Resources

■ ■ ■ ■ ■ ■ ■ ■ ■ ■ **top tip** ■ ■ ■ ■ ■ ■ ■ ■ ■ ■

Me and Us.com

Many of the key resources for use with people with learning disabilities are now out of print. A website has been set up holding some of these resources which can be bought and downloaded.

Some are already on the website others will be added, the website is:

www.me-and-us.com

and at present has:

- *Chance to choose – sexuality and relationships education for people with learning difficulties* Dixon, 1992 (discontinued, will be a new edition in 2003).

  An educator's resource book for professionals working with people with learning difficulties. Contains background information, a carefully developed scheme of work, practical activities, lesson plans and a wealth of resources.

- *On the agenda: sex education for young people with learning difficulties* Scott, 1995.

  A guide to policy-making, planning and working with young people in schools and colleges using drama and active learning methods.

- *Picture yourself* Craft and Dixon.

  A teaching resource around social and sex education specifically designed to be used with people with learning disabilities. Four sets of 48 drawings and photographs per set with teachers' notes.

Resources for staff have been put into the sections of this publication that they correspond to. They are not a definitive list, many staff said they were used to adapting mainstream publications for use with groups and different staff liked different types of resource. The key is to see examples of what is available and what you can find locally. Contact your local Health Promotion Unit to see what they currently have in their library.

"I have gained a wide base of facts and resources not known to me already."

Resources for people with a learning disability

AVAILABLE FROM BILD
Wolverhampton Road, Kidderminster, Worcs. DY10 3PP, tel 01752 202301

- *I want to be a good parent* McGaw, 1995.
  A set of 5 illustrated booklets and audio tapes giving practical advice.

- *Your good health*, 1998.
  Set of 12 booklets about health issues including childbirth and sex.

AVAILABLE FROM BROOK PUBLICATIONS
PO Box 1239, Coventry CV8 3ZB, tel 024 76 545557

- *Learning to love* Fraser, 1997.
  A set of five booklets including sex, contraception and health and infection.

AVAILABLE FROM CALEDONIA YOUTH
5 Castle Terrace, Edinburgh EN1 2DP, tel 0131 229 3596

- *A visit to a Brook Centre* 1999.
  A fully illustrated booklet about seeking contraception.

- *Thinking about sex? How to use condoms* 1999.
  A fully illustrated booklet to explain when, where and how to use condoms.

AVAILABLE FROM CHANGE NORTH
Units 19/20, Unity Business Centre, 26 Roundhay Road, Leeds, tel 0113 243 0202

- *Planning a baby*
- *Depo Provera*

  Booklets with clear illustrations and simple language looking at the above subjects.

AVAILABLE FROM THE ELFRIDA SOCIETY
34 Islington Park Street, London, N1 1PX, tel 020 7359 7443

- **Cathy has thrush**
- **Period problems**
- **Hysterectomy (x2)**

  Booklets with colour diagrams on the above subjects.

AVAILABLE FROM NHS CANCER SCREENING PROGRAMMES
The Manor House, 260 Eccleshall Road, Sheffield, S11 9PS, tel 0114 271 1060

- **Having a smear test**
- **Good practice in breast and cervical screening for women with learning disabilities**

AVAILABLE FROM PAVILION PUBLICATIONS
The Ironworks, Cheapside, Brighton, BN1 4GD, tel 01273 623222
www.pavpub.com

- **Becoming a woman** Cooper, 2000
  A teaching pack on menstruation for young women.

- **Making the change** Cooper and Welsh, 2001
  A teaching pack on the menopause for women.

- **Supporting women with learning disabilities through the menopause**
  McCarthy and Millard, 2003
  Video and training pack on the menopause for use with women with learning disabilities and their carers.

AVAILABLE FROM PEOPLE FIRST
207/215 Kings Cross Road, London WC1X 9DB, tel 020 7485 6660

- **Everything you ever wanted to know about safer sex ... but nobody bothered to tell you** Nigel Bull with Camden People First, 1993.
  Contains information about having safe sex and the prevention of HIV and AIDS.

AVAILABLE FROM ROYAL COLLEGE OF PSYCHIATRISTS
17 Belgrave Square, London, SW1X 8PG, tel 020 7235 2351 x146
www.rcpsych.ac.uk/publications

- **Books beyond words** Collins, 1993.
  Illustrated booklets designed to enable people to understand health issues and personal relationships.

FREE downloadable resources!

There are some other websites which now provide free access to downloadable resources which can be highly useful.

Some of these are:

- ### *www.howitis.org.uk*

  Resource:
  An image vocabulary developed to help children communicate about a range of issues including sexuality

- ### *www.doh.gov.uk*

  Resources:
  Lots of downloadable documents including:

  12 key points of consent: the law in England
  Seeking consent working with people with learning disabilities

- ### *www.ncb.org.uk/sef*

  Resources:
  Ensuring entitlement: sex and relationships education for disabled children
  Sex and relationships: education resources for children with disabilities

- ### *www.hda-online.org.uk*

  Resources:
  Health-related resources for people with learning disabilities,
  Health Education Authority, 1999.

  Lots of other downloadable information as well.

- ### *www.teenagepregnancyunit.gov.uk*

  Lots of downloadable resources.

*"I know where I need to go
for resources."*

Contacts

<!-- decorative large "9" -->

Organisation	What it does	Contact details
fpa	**fpa** is the only registered charity working to improve the sexual health and reproductive rights of all people throughout the UK by: ● Providing information ● Developing publications ● Campaigning and lobbying ● Working in the community ● Delivering training and consultancy **fpa** also runs training courses for staff working with adults and young people with learning disabilities	**fpa** 2–12 Pentonville Road London N1 9FP tel: 020 7923 5246 fax: 020 7837 3042 e-mail: clairef@fpa.org.uk website: www.fpa.org.uk To order **fpa** resources or for a free mail order catalogue, contact **fpa direct** on 01865 719418 For a training brochure ring 020 7923 5235/5232
Ann Craft Trust	National organisation working with adults and children with a learning disability who may be at risk of abuse	ACT Centre for Social Work University Park Nottingham NG7 2RD tel: 0115 951 5400 e-mail: communityaction@ nottingham.ac.uk website: www.nottingham.ac.uk/ sociology/act/Pub.html

Organisation	What it does	Contact details
Association for Residential Care (ARC)	ARC is an umbrella organisation which brings together those who provide for people with learning disabilities	ARC House Marsden Street, Chesterfield Derbyshire S40 1JY tel: 01246 555043 e-mail: contact.us@arcuk.org.uk website: www.arcuk.org.uk
British Institute for Learning Disabilities (BILD)	Committed to improving the quality of life of all people with learning disabilities	British Institute of Learning Disabilities Campion House Green Street, Kidderminster Worcestershire DY10 1JL tel: 01562 72301 Publication sales: 01752 202301 fax: 01562 723029 e-mail: enquiries@bild.org.uk website: www.bild.org.uk
Department of Health	To improve the health and well-being of people in England	The Department of Health Richmond House 79 Whitehall London SW1A 2NS tel: 020 7972 4499 e-mail: dhmail@doh.gsi.gov.uk website: www.doh.gov.uk
Down's Syndrome Association	National organisation concerned with all aspects of Down's Syndrome	The Down's Syndrome Association 155 Mitcham Rd London SW17 9PG tel: 020 8682 4001 fax: 020 8682 4012 e-mail: info@downs-syndrome.org.uk website: www.dsa-uk.com

Organisation	What it does	Contact details
Foundation for people with learning disabilities	Aims to improve the quality of life for people with learning disabilities, by conducting research and sharing the findings with other people.	UK Office 7th Floor 83 Victoria Street London SW1H 0HW tel: 020 7802 0300 fax: 020 7802 0301 e-mail: fpld@fpld.org.uk website: www.learningdisabilities.org.uk
Image In Action	Creative work with young people and adults with learning disabilities	Chinnor Road Bledlow Ridge High Wycombe HP14 4AJ tel: 01494 481 632 e-mail: iia@nascr.net
LDUK	Web-based site containing latest news and events information in the UK	e-mail: LDUK@ Learningdisabilitiesuk.org.uk website: www.learningdisabilitiesuk. org.uk
Mencap	To provide support for people with learning disabilities in all aspects of their lives	Mencap National Centre 123 Golden Lane London EC1Y 0RT tel: 020 7454 0454 fax: 020 7608 3254 helpline: 0845 6040600 e-mail: information@mencap.org.uk website: www.mencap.org.uk
National Autistic Society	Aims to encourage better understanding of autism and to pioneer specialist services	393 City Road London EC1V 1NG tel: 020 7833 2299 fax: 020 7833 9666 e-mail: nas@nas.org.uk website: www.nas.org.uk

Organisation	What it does	Contact details
National Development Team – NDT	An independent not for profit development agency that wants new opportunities and inclusion in ordinary life for all people with learning disabilities	Albion Wharf Albion Street Manchester M1 5LN tel: 0161 228 7055 fax: 0161 228 7059 e-mail: office@ndt.org.uk website: www.ndt.org.uk
Norah Fry Research Centre	The Centre was established in 1988 as part of the University of Bristol's Department of Mental Health. Its principal interests are the evaluation and development of services for people with learning disabilities	Norah Fry Research Centre 3 Priory Road Bristol BS8 1TX tel: 0117 923 8137 fax: 0117 946 6553 website: www.bris.ac.uk/ Depts/NorahFry
Paradigm	Consultancy and development agency formed by people with experience in inclusion, health, social services and community care	Paradigm 8 Brandon Street Birkenhead CH41 5HN tel: 0870 010 4933 fax: 0870 010 4934 e-mail: admin@paradigm-uk.org website: www.paradigm-uk.org
Respond	National organisation working with people with learning disabilities who have been sexually abused	3rd Floor 24–32 Stephenson Way London NW1 2HD tel: 020 7383 0700 fax: 020 7387 1222 helpline: 0845 606 1503 e-mail: admin@respond.org.uk website: www.respond.org.uk

Organisation	What it does	Contact details
Sex Education Forum	The national authority on sex and relationships education	National Children's Bureau 8 Wakley Street London, EC1V 7QE tel: 020 7843 6052 fax: 020 7843 6053 e-mail: sexedforum@ncb.org.uk website: www.ncb.org.uk/sef
The Tizard Centre	One of the leading UK academic groups in the UK working in learning disabilities	Tizard Centre University of Kent at Canterbury Beverley Farm Canterbury Kent CT2 7LZ tel: 01227 764000 fax: 01227 763674 e-mail: Tizard-gen@ukc.ac.uk website: www.ukc.ac.uk/tizard
Values into Action	UK-wide campaign with people with learning disabilities	Oxford House Derbyshire Street Bethnal Green London E2 6HG tel: 020 7729 5436 e-mail: general@viauk.org website: www.viauk.org
Working with Words	Produce information and literature for people with learning disabilities	St Mary's Gallery Greenlaw Street Woolwich London SE18 5AR tel: 020 8855 6644 fax: 020 8855 3393 e-mail: workingwith@ words01.fsnet.co.uk